GW00857470

The camping holiday

and other stories

Illustrated by Nina O'Connell

Nelson

The camping holiday

One day Jip said,

"Let's go and see my friend Tom.

We can go and camp on his farm."

"Oh yes," said Pat.

"That will be fun."

So Ben put the tent in the car and
Sam put in his sun hat.
Meg put in a pan and
Pat put in his fishing rod.
They all got in the car and
went to the farm.

"Here we are," said Jip.
"Let's put the tent up
under this tree," said Deb.
"I will go and find
my friend Tom," said Jip.

Ben and Sam put up the tent.
Meg went to get some twigs and
Pat went to get some water.
Deb sat by the fire and
wrote a letter to
her friend Tim.

"Shall I catch some fish
for tea?" said Pat.
"Yes, go and catch some fish.
I will make a cup of tea," said Meg.
Ben put the pan on the fire
to cook the fish.

Just then he felt a drop
on his nose.
"Oh dear," said Ben.
"It is going to rain."
And it did.
It rained and it rained
and it rained.

The fire went out and the water
dripped from the tree and
the tent fell down.
"Oh dear," said Pat.
"I am cold and I am wet and
I want to go home."

Just then Jip came back with Tom.

"Hello," said Tom.

"You do look sad and
you do look wet.

Do you want to come to my house?"

"Yes, please," said the friends.

So they all went to Tom's house
and had Pat's fish for tea.

Who will win?

Pat the pig had a new football.
He wanted to play football
with his friends.

"Will you play with me, Sam?"
said Pat.
"Yes," said Sam.
"I can run very fast."

"Will you play with me, Ben?"
said Pat.
"Yes, I will," said Ben.
"I can kick very hard."

So they all went out
to play a game of football.
Jip blew the whistle and
the game began.

Ben kicked the ball to Sam.

Sam kicked the ball to Jip.

Pat ran very fast but

he was too late.

Jip kicked the ball into the net.

"One for us," said Jip.

Now Meg kicked the ball.

Pat ran after it.

He picked up the ball and

threw it to Deb.

"You can't do that, Pat,"

said Ben.

"You must kick the ball."

Then it was Deb's turn.
She kicked the ball but
it did not go very far.
Pat ran up very fast.
He kicked the ball hard.
Sam wanted to help him but
Pat was too fast.

"Run, run," said Ben.

"Shoot, shoot," said Sam.

Pat kicked the ball
right into the net.

"I've won the game," he said.

And he had.

Meg's birthday present

It was Meg's birthday.

Deb gave her some paper.

Jip gave her a football book.

Pat gave her a red bonnet.

Ben gave her a bat.

The postman came with
some birthday cards.

Meg opened her cards.

The friends played musical chairs
and ate jam sandwiches.

Pat had ten sandwiches.

They played hide-and-seek.
Deb hid in a box and
fell fast asleep.
Sam came late and
gave Meg a blue ball.

They played pig-in-the-middle.
Pat the pig was very good at it.
He was not often in the middle.
Then they all went home.

The next day Meg did not feel well.

She went to bed and

the doctor came to see her.

"I know what is the matter," he said.

He told Meg to stay in bed.

All Meg's friends gave her
something for her birthday.
She gave them something too.
She gave them . . . **chicken pox**.